The Family History

ESSAY BY SUSAN REED

The Oxford Illustrated Press

©The Oxford Illustrated Press 1981
Printed by Haynes Publishing Group,
Sparkford, Yeovil, Somerset, England
Bound by Kemp Hall, Oxford, England
ISBN 0 902280 84 8

Oxford Illustrated Press Limited,
Sparkford, Yeovil,
Somerset, BA22 7JJ

This book belongs to:

_____

Signed: _____

Date: _____

The Family History is for those of us who are interested in the lives of our relations and ancestors, who want to be able to start writing straightaway, and who would like a specially bound book to be able to record our findings in.

1. Turn to page 7.

2. Decide who you are going to choose as your first subject. If for example, you decide to begin with yourself, do the following:

3. Next to the word 'Name:', write your own name.

4. Next to 'Son, daughter of:', write the names of your parents.

5. Next to 'Brother, sister to:', write the names of your brothers and sisters.

6. Next to 'Husband, wife of:', if married, write the name of your husband or wife.

7. Next to 'Date of Birth and Marriage:', write when and where you were born, and if married, when and where the ceremony took place.

8. By 'Children:', write the names of any children you may have.

9. By 'Childhood:', write as much as you can about your childhood and schooldays.

10. By 'Adult Life:', write as much as you can about your life since finishing your education.

11. Turn to page 6. You can either use this page just for sticking in photographs, cuttings or other memorabilia for illustration, or you can combine these with addresses and other notes to supplement page 7.

12. When you have completed your entry, turn to page 5, the Contents page. Under the heading 'Member of Family', and alongside 'page 7', write your name.

You have now begun your book.

When you have completed your *Family History*, you will have a unique book that can not only be enjoyed by yourself today, but which will be treasured by your children and grandchildren as it is passed down the generations.

CONTENTS

Name: _____

Son, daughter of: _____

Brother, sister to: _____

Husband, wife of: _____

Date and Place of Birth: _____

Marriage: _____

Death: _____

Children: _____

CHILDHOOD: _____

_____

_____

_____

_____

_____

_____

ADULT LIFE: _____

_____

_____

_____

_____

_____

_____

_____

_____

_____

_____

_____

_____

_____

_____

Name: _____

Son, daughter of: _____

Brother, sister to: _____

Husband, wife of: _____

Date and Place of Birth: _____

Marriage: _____

Death: _____

Children: _____

CHILDHOOD: _____

_____

_____

_____

_____

_____

_____

_____

ADULT LIFE: _____

_____

_____

_____

_____

_____

_____

_____

_____

_____

_____

_____

_____

_____

_____

_____

_____

Name: _____

Son, daughter of: _____

Brother, sister to: _____

Husband, wife of: _____

Date and Place of Birth: _____

Marriage: _____

Death: _____

Children: _____

CHILDHOOD: _____

_____

_____

_____

_____

_____

_____

ADULT LIFE: _____

_____

_____

_____

_____

_____

_____

_____

_____

_____

_____

_____

_____

_____

_____

Name: _____

Son, daughter of: _____

Brother, sister to: _____

Husband, wife of: _____

Date and Place of Birth: _____

Marriage: _____

Death: _____

Children: _____

CHILDHOOD: _____

_____

_____

_____

_____

_____

_____

ADULT LIFE: _____

_____

_____

_____

_____

_____

_____

_____

_____

_____

_____

_____

_____

_____

_____

_____

Name: _____

Son, daughter of: _____

Brother, sister to: _____

Husband, wife of: _____

Date and Place of Birth: _____

Marriage: _____

Death: _____

Children: _____

CHILDHOOD: _____

_____

_____

_____

_____

_____

_____

_____

ADULT LIFE: _____

_____

_____

_____

_____

_____

_____

_____

_____

_____

_____

_____

_____

_____

_____

Name: _____

Son, daughter of: _____

Brother, sister to: _____

Husband, wife of: _____

Date and Place of Birth: _____

Marriage: _____

Death: _____

Children: _____

CHILDHOOD: _____

_____

_____

_____

_____

_____

_____

ADULT LIFE: _____

_____

_____

_____

_____

_____

_____

_____

_____

_____

_____

_____

_____

_____

_____

_____

_____

Name: _____

Son, daughter of: _____

Brother, sister to: _____

Husband, wife of: _____

Date and Place of Birth: _____

Marriage: _____

Death: _____

Children: _____

CHILDHOOD: _____

_____

_____

_____

_____

_____

_____

_____

ADULT LIFE: _____

_____

_____

_____

_____

_____

_____

_____

_____

_____

_____

_____

_____

_____

_____

_____

_____

Name: _____

Son, daughter of: _____

Brother, sister to: _____

Husband, wife of: _____

Date and Place of Birth: _____

Marriage: _____

Death: _____

Children: _____

CHILDHOOD: _____

_____

_____

_____

_____

_____

_____

ADULT LIFE: _____

_____

_____

_____

_____

_____

_____

_____

_____

_____

_____

_____

_____

_____

_____

_____

Name: _____

Son, daughter of: _____

Brother, sister to: _____

Husband, wife of: _____

Date and Place of Birth: _____

Marriage: _____

Death: _____

Children: _____

CHILDHOOD: _____

_____

_____

_____

_____

_____

_____

_____

ADULT LIFE: _____

_____

_____

_____

_____

_____

_____

_____

_____

_____

_____

_____

_____

_____

_____

Name: _____

Son, daughter of: _____

Brother, sister to: _____

Husband, wife of: _____

Date and Place of Birth: _____

Marriage: _____

Death: _____

Children: _____

CHILDHOOD: _____

_____

_____

_____

_____

_____

_____

ADULT LIFE: _____

_____

_____

_____

_____

_____

_____

_____

_____

_____

_____

_____

_____

_____

Name: _____

Son, daughter of: _____

Brother, sister to: _____

Husband, wife of: _____

Date and Place of Birth: _____

Marriage: _____

Death: _____

Children: _____

CHILDHOOD: _____

_____

_____

_____

_____

_____

_____

ADULT LIFE: _____

_____

_____

_____

_____

_____

_____

_____

_____

_____

_____

_____

_____

_____

_____

Name: _____

Son, daughter of: _____

Brother, sister to: _____

Husband, wife of: _____

Date and Place of Birth: _____

Marriage: _____

Death: _____

Children: _____

CHILDHOOD: _____

_____

_____

_____

_____

_____

_____

ADULT LIFE: _____

_____

_____

_____

_____

_____

_____

_____

_____

_____

_____

_____

_____

_____

_____

_____

Name: _____

Son, daughter of: _____

Brother, sister to: _____

Husband, wife of: _____

Date and Place of Birth: _____

Marriage: _____

Death: _____

Children: _____

CHILDHOOD: _____

_____

_____

_____

_____

_____

_____

_____

ADULT LIFE: _____

_____

_____

_____

_____

_____

_____

_____

_____

_____

_____

_____

_____

_____

_____

_____

_____

Name: _____

Son, daughter of: _____

Brother, sister to: _____

Husband, wife of: _____

Date and Place of Birth: _____

Marriage: _____

Death: _____

Children: _____

CHILDHOOD: _____

_____

_____

_____

_____

_____

_____

_____

ADULT LIFE: _____

_____

_____

_____

_____

_____

_____

_____

_____

_____

_____

_____

_____

_____

_____

_____

_____

_____

Name: _____

Son, daughter of: _____

Brother, sister to: _____

Husband, wife of: _____

Date and Place of Birth: _____

Marriage: _____

Death: _____

Children: _____

CHILDHOOD: _____

_____

_____

_____

_____

_____

_____

ADULT LIFE: _____

_____

_____

_____

_____

_____

_____

_____

_____

_____

_____

_____

_____

_____

_____

_____

Name: _____

Son, daughter of: _____

Brother, sister to: _____

Husband, wife of: _____

Date and Place of Birth: _____

Marriage: _____

Death: _____

Children: _____

CHILDHOOD: _____

_____

_____

_____

_____

_____

_____

_____

ADULT LIFE: _____

_____

_____

_____

_____

_____

_____

_____

_____

_____

_____

_____

_____

_____

_____

_____

_____

Name: _____

Son, daughter of: _____

Brother, sister to: _____

Husband, wife of: _____

Date and Place of Birth: _____

Marriage: _____

Death: _____

Children: _____

CHILDHOOD: _____

_____

_____

_____

_____

_____

_____

_____

ADULT LIFE: _____

_____

_____

_____

_____

_____

_____

_____

_____

_____

_____

_____

_____

_____

_____

_____

_____

Name: _____

Son, daughter of: _____

Brother, sister to: _____

Husband, wife of: _____

Date and Place of Birth: _____

Marriage: _____

Death: _____

Children: _____

CHILDHOOD: _____

_____

_____

_____

_____

_____

_____

ADULT LIFE: _____

_____

_____

_____

_____

_____

_____

_____

_____

_____

_____

_____

_____

_____

_____

_____

Name: _____

Son, daughter of: _____

Brother, sister to: _____

Husband, wife of: _____

Date and Place of Birth: _____

Marriage: _____

Death: _____

Children: _____

CHILDHOOD: _____

_____

_____

_____

_____

_____

_____

ADULT LIFE: _____

_____

_____

_____

_____

_____

_____

_____

_____

_____

_____

_____

_____

_____

Name: _____

Son, daughter of: _____

Brother, sister to: _____

Husband, wife of: _____

Date and Place of Birth: _____

Marriage: _____

Death: _____

Children: _____

CHILDHOOD: _____

_____

_____

_____

_____

_____

_____

ADULT LIFE: _____

_____

_____

_____

_____

_____

_____

_____

_____

_____

_____

_____

_____

_____

_____

_____

Name: _____

Son, daughter of: _____

Brother, sister to: _____

Husband, wife of: _____

Date and Place of Birth: _____

_____ Marriage: _____

_____ Death: _____

Children: _____

CHILDHOOD: _____

_____

_____

_____

_____

_____

_____

ADULT LIFE: _____

_____

_____

_____

_____

_____

_____

_____

_____

_____

_____

_____

_____

_____

_____

_____

Name: _____

Son, daughter of: _____

Brother, sister to: _____

Husband, wife of: _____

Date and Place of Birth: _____

Marriage: _____

Death: _____

Children: _____

CHILDHOOD: _____

_____

_____

_____

_____

_____

_____

ADULT LIFE: _____

_____

_____

_____

_____

_____

_____

_____

_____

_____

_____

_____

_____

_____

_____

_____

Name: _____

Son, daughter of: _____

Brother, sister to: _____

Husband, wife of: _____

Date and Place of Birth: _____

Marriage: _____

Death: _____

Children: _____

CHILDHOOD: _____

_____

_____

_____

_____

_____

_____

ADULT LIFE: _____

_____

_____

_____

_____

_____

_____

_____

_____

_____

_____

_____

_____

_____

_____

_____

Name: _____

Son, daughter of: _____

Brother, sister to: _____

Husband, wife of: _____

Date and Place of Birth: _____

Marriage: _____

Death: _____

Children: _____

CHILDHOOD: _____

_____

_____

_____

_____

_____

_____

_____

ADULT LIFE: _____

_____

_____

_____

_____

_____

_____

_____

_____

_____

_____

_____

_____

_____

_____

_____

Name: _____

Son, daughter of: _____

Brother, sister to: _____

Husband, wife of: _____

Date and Place of Birth: _____

Marriage: _____

Death: _____

Children: _____

CHILDHOOD: _____

_____

_____

_____

_____

_____

_____

ADULT LIFE: _____

_____

_____

_____

_____

_____

_____

_____

_____

_____

_____

_____

_____

_____

_____

Name: _____

Son, daughter of: _____

Brother, sister to: _____

Husband, wife of: _____

Date and Place of Birth: _____

Marriage: _____

Death: _____

Children: _____

CHILDHOOD: _____

_____

_____

_____

_____

_____

_____

_____

ADULT LIFE: _____

_____

_____

_____

_____

_____

_____

_____

_____

_____

_____

_____

_____

_____

_____

_____

_____

Name: _____

Son, daughter of: _____

Brother, sister to: _____

Husband, wife of: _____

Date and Place of Birth: _____

Marriage: _____

Death: _____

Children: _____

CHILDHOOD: _____

_____

_____

_____

_____

_____

_____

ADULT LIFE: _____

_____

_____

_____

_____

_____

_____

_____

_____

_____

_____

_____

_____

_____

_____

_____

_____

Compiling your family history can be fun. Here are some hints to help you begin.

Ask the Family

It sounds obvious but the first step is to ask the older members of the family (grandparents, aunts, uncles etc.) what they can tell you about their parents and grandparents.

Very often it can be difficult to locate long-lost aunts and uncles but there are a number of approaches you can use to tackle this problem. If you have a last-known address, write to 'The Occupier' at that address, enquiring of the where-abouts of the person you are seeking. If you have no address at all but have the name of the village or small town in which the person lives, you could try looking in a telephone directory. If this yields nothing, consider visiting the area and asking at the local public house or corner shop–two certain sources of infor-mation about local people.

Of course it may not be possible for you to visit the area, or perhaps you have only the name of a large town or city. In that case, try writing a friendly letter to the local newspaper ('Letters to the Edi-tor' page), appealing for anyone knowing the present whereabouts of your relative (or the last known address) to contact you. The Letters page is likely to be more successful than an advertisement in the Personal Column.

Assuming you are able to find the relative you are seeking you must be careful to ask the sort of questions which will lead to the information you need. This requires careful forethought on your part. You should be aiming to find out as much detail as possible–especially dates of birth, marriage and death–on as many of your ancestors as possible, together with any interesting personal anecdotes. You could also try to locate the Family Bible, certificates of birth, marriage and death, wills, apprenticeship indentures, personal letters, and family photographs. All of these can be interesting and can provide useful information.

The best way to approach an interview with an elderly relative is to list your questions (in order of priority) before your visit. Do bear in mind, however, that the person you are talking to will be eager to relate favourite family stories rather than giving you the names, dates and places you are looking for. You should try to 'steer' the conversation as much as possible without appearing to be rude and losing the interest of the interviewee. Remember that you may need to return on another occasion for some further information.

In the event of a relative living too far away for a visit, it is a good idea to prepare a questionnaire for him/her to complete and return to you. For this purpose, the following questions might be suitable:

1. Do you know where and when
...................(name of ancestor)

   i   was born or baptised
   ii   was married
   iii died/is buried
2. Did he/she have any brothers or sis-ters?
If so, where did they live? Are they still alive?
What can you remember about them?
3. Do you have any certificates of birth, marriage or death for any of your rela-tives?
4. Do you know of the existence of any wills in the family?
5. With which religion were the family connected?
6. Do you have any old photographs, family letters, diaries, wills, relating to any members of the family?
7. Was there a Family Bible at any time? If so, where is it likely to be now?
8. Does tradition say that the family orig-inated from any particular part of the British Isles?
9. Is there a family grave?
10. Do you know any other member of the family who might be able to give me some information about my ancestors?

Tombstones and Burial Records

There is a lot of useful information to be had from the tombstones of your an-cestors. If you know the parish or village where your ancestors are buried it is worthwhile taking a trip to the local churchyard to look for any tombstones bearing the surname you are interested in. You may be lucky and find not only those you have gone in search of, but many others relating to other members of the family; but do beware of assuming relationships before they are proven.

You may find the tombstone is covered in moss. Do not let this deter you–a stiff brush will remove the moss to reveal the inscription underneath. The person's age and date of death will be on the stone and this of course will lead you to the year of birth. Unless there is only one person in the grave, relationships of those buried there will be shown. Should the stone be difficult to read, contact the Vicar of the church and ask to see the Burial Regis-ters.

You may need to visit a Record Office at this stage of your research, as the Vicar may well have handed over his records to their care. Record Offices exist for every county and in many cities, and your local library should be able to tell you the nearest Record Office for the town or village you are researching. Research there is free of charge but you will need to check the times of opening.

Some of your ancestors will be buried in public cemeteries rather than churchyards. Public cemeteries have been in existence from about 1850 so any relative who died after 1850 may well be interred in a cemetery. You will be able to find out from the Parks and Recreations Department of the Local Council where the nearest cemetery is and what date it opened. You should then make arrange-ments with the Cemetery Records Keeper

to consult the burial records held there. These records will tell you the date of burial, the age of the deceased and the names of others in the same grave. (One grave can contain as many as 12 people and most of them will be related). The Cemetery Keeper will be able to show you where the grave is.

Wills

Wills for those who died after 1858 are fairly easy to obtain. They are all regis-tered with the Principal Probate Registry at Somerset House, The Strand, London WC2. Copies can be obtained from that address, of any will for any person from any area of England or Wales, on pay-ment of the appropriate fee. The District Probate Registry has copies of all the wills proved at that particular office and copies can be obtained or searches carried out there.

The first step is to find out the approx-imate year in which the person died and then to search the indexes to the wills for that period. These indexes (arranged alphabetically) are usually kept at the District Probate Registry offices but some of them may have been transferred to the nearest Record Office so you should tele-phone first to find the exact location. Entries in the index are detailed enough to ensure that you find the correct entry (should a will exist). Once you have found the entry in the index you will be able to ask for a copy of the will, for which there will be a charge.

It may be that your ancestors did not leave a will but did leave Letters of Administration (known as Admons) giv-ing permission to the relatives to dispose of any assets. Admons are sometimes indexed separately so be careful to check. Whilst these do not contain very much personal information they can contain useful names and addresses.

Searching for wills before 1858 is somewhat complex. These early wills were looked after by the church and came under various types of jurisdiction. A number of guides to finding early wills have been published and these should be consulted at your nearest Record Office or Local History Library. The wills them-selves are mainly housed at Record Of-fices and copies can be obtained, provid-ing you have sufficient information to locate the will.

Printed Directories

From about 1750 onwards a number of directories were published covering most parts of the country. These directories give a short description of each town and village with lists of the occupants, their addresses and their occupations. They vary in the amount of detail but occu-pants are listed alphabetically by sur-name, so they are quick and easy to consult. They are useful when trying to find the exact place of residence of an ancestor or his/her occupation. There exist a number of trade and professional directories relating to the clergy, the legal profession and the military. You should ask at your Local History Library or Record Office for details.

Certificates of Birth, Marriage and Death

From July 1837 onwards, it was a legal requirement in England and Wales that every birth, marriage and death should be registered. The central repository for this information is now St Catherines House, Aldwych, London WC1. Members of the public are allowed to search the alphabetically arranged indexes free of charge. The indexes, however, give only the briefest information and are only useful in leading you to the relevant certificate. The charge for purchasing a certificate at St Catherines House is currently £4. Certificates can be obtained by post at a current charge of £8.

District Registration offices have records of certificates for their own District and members of the public can search there, but the charge is £10 for up to six hours' continuous searching. The cost of purchasing a certificate is £4.

Whilst it can be seen that certificates are costly, they provide a reliable source of information for dates, addresses, relationships and occupations. No family tree can be completed without them, so every effort should be made to locate those still in existence within your family.

The following information is shown on each certificate:
Birth certificate Name, sex, date and place of birth; name, address and occupation of father; name and maiden surname of mother; particulars of the informant, date of registration.
Marriage certificate The date and place of marriage, the names of those being married, their age, previous marital status, occupation, residence at the time of marriage; fathers' names and occupation.
Death certificate Name, sex, age and occupation of the deceased; place, date and cause of death; particulars of the informant.

When you are considering making a search within a Registration office try to remember the following points:
1.You should wear lightweight casual clothing. The indexes you will be using will be heavy and dusty, making the work hot and uncomfortable.
2.You should prepare well before hand so that you can use your search time efficiently. You should not spend valuable time at the Registration office looking through your papers to plan your research.
3.The entry you are looking for may be shown under a different spelling from the one you expected to find e.g. Reed, Read, Reid, Reede, Rhead, etc.
4.A birth may be registered up to six

weeks after it has taken place.
5.If you are looking for a common name you will need to have reliable detailed information to help you to locate the entry. A name like Stephen Jackson can occur several times within the same registration area during the same quarter of the year.
6.You may not need to buy a death certificate if you can find where the person is buried – the details on the stone or within the burial records may be adequate.

Censuses

Censuses have been taken every ten years since 1801. The earliest censuses contain merely population figures and are of no use to the family historian but those of 1841, 1851, 1861, and 1871 are of very great use. Censuses are only made available for consultation by the public 100 years after their preparation for reasons of confidentiality. The 1881 census will be made available in 1982.

The 1841 census shows the names of all persons in each household, ages to the nearest 5 years (with exact ages for children under 15), occupations, and whether the person was born within the same county in which they are living at the time of the census. From 1851 onwards exact ages are given for all, marital status is shown, relationship to head of household is given together with the parish of birth.

Censuses can be used to find information on persons born before 1800 and can therefore take your research back into the eighteenth century. The census returns have been microfilmed and are available for viewing on a microfilm reader at libraries and Record Offices. The Public Record Office in Portugal Street, London WC1 has the censuses for the whole of England and Wales available for public consultation. (Prior application for a Readers Ticket is necessary).

If your research is based on a village or a small town it will not take too much time to look through the reel of microfilm for the whole village in order to track down the family you want. The details which will come to light in such a search will build up an interesting picture of life during the nineteenth century. However, if your ancestors lived in a large town or city you will need to know their address–or at least the district–so that you can turn to the relevant section of microfilm. It is useful to refer to directories for this purpose. To work through several reels of film in search of a family is tiring and time consuming.

Parish Registers

From the sixteenth century until 1837 the only system of recording a baptism, a

marriage or a burial, was through the church records. Whilst many of your ancestors may not have been members of the established church they would have been obliged by law at certain times to register such events at their nearest Parish Church. From 1754 to 1837 no marriage was legal unless registered by the Parish Church.

Each church kept registers and these (or copies of them) can be found either at the church itself or (more likely) at the relevant Record Office. The information contained within the registers varies considerably according to the conscientiousness or otherwise of the incumbent but the following can be taken as a rough guide.

A *baptismal register* will give the name of the child, the name of the father (and usually the mother), the occupation of the father and (very often) the place of abode.

A *marriage register* gives the names and ages of the two people, occupations and place of abode. For later years the names of witnesses are included.

A *burial register* very often gives only the name of the deceased and the date of burial though the registers for the nineteenth century give more detail.

Bishops Transcripts are copies of the original registers which were sent annually to the Bishop and these can usually be seen at Record Offices. In some cases church registers have been published in book form or typed copies have been made. These can be much easier to consult, though not as interesting to work with as the original registers. Some printed registers include an alphabetical index of entries which can be used as a quick reference to locate a name.

It is generally the case now that church registers and their copies are being handed over to Record Offices. This should be the first place you enquire when looking for registers and also for parish records such as Poor Records, and Churchwardens Accounts, which can both be useful sources.

Family History Societies

If you should decide to continue researching your family history then make a point of joining your local Family History Society. There are branches in most large towns and cities. Ask at your local library for details. Most societies hold monthly meetings, usually with speakers on special topics. There is also an opportunity for you to meet with others sharing your interest and to exchange information. A newsletter is sent out every 2-3 months with items of local interest. Membership fees are around £3.50 a year.